W
Guide to Life

Also by Tess Read

Mr Benn's Little Book of Life

The Wombles'
Guide to Life

Tess Read

arrow books

First published by Arrow in 2003

1 3 5 7 9 10 8 6 4 2

Arrow
The Random House Group Limited
20 Vauxhall Bridge Road, London SW1V 2SA

Random House Australia (Pty) Limited
20 Alfred Street, Milsons Point, Sydney,
New South Wales 2061, Australia

Random House New Zealand Limited
18 Poland Road, Glenfield, Auckland 10, New Zealand

Random House (Pty) Limited
Endulini, 5a Jubilee Road, Parktown 2193, South Africa

The Random House Group Limited Reg. No. 954009

www.randomhouse.co.uk

A CIP catalogue record for this book is available
from the British Library

Papers used by Random House are natural, recyclable products made from
wood grown in sustainable forests. The manufacturing processes conform
to the environmental regulations of the country of origin

Design/Make up by Roger Walker
Printed and bound in Denmark by Nørhaven Book, Viborg

ISBN 0 09 946339 3

Author photograph by Ian Brunton

Contents

Elisabeth Beresford

Tess Read

Author's Note

The Wombles are the creation of prolific children's story teller, Elisabeth Beresford, who had the idea when out walking in Wimbledon one day with her young children who wanted to know who lived on 'Wombledon' Common. Elisabeth wrote many Womble story books (and some of these tales feature in this book) before the BBC commissioned 60 TV episodes each of which seemed much longer than their actual 5 minutes.

The Wombles were broadcast around the world and their fame spread from Europe to Australia, New Zealand and even Asia – they were big in Japan. The books have been a hit in several different languages including such classic titles as *De Wombels op Stap*. The Wombles were relaunched in 1996 by Cinar, with new characters, such as Stepney Womble.

No one who lived through the '70s could forget Mike Batt as an all-singing all-dancing Orinoco on

Top of the Pops singing the hit songs
'Underground, overground, Wombling free'
and 'Remember you're a Womble.' Also
unforgettable was the wonderful
voice of the Wombles – Bernard
Cribbins who captured the
Wombles' essence so perfectly,
from the high faux French
voice of Madame Cholet,
the cheery bluster of
Great Uncle Bulgaria,
and the comedy of
Orinoco.

Acknowledgements

Thanks are due to Edgar Hodges not only for permission to use his wonderful artwork but also for rescuing it all from the dark recesses of his loft. Thanks also to Cinar for permission to use the stills. For all their different and excellent help in making this book come about great thanks are due to Danny, as ever, Joe, surprisingly, Roger, of course, Clare, again, Vanessa and Jane, for the first time, and Tony, with bells on. I would also like to pay tribute to the hot chocolate of the Bean 'n' Cup and the cakes of Patisserie Valerie. And above all thank you, Liza, for creating the Wombles.

Wombles' names from around the world

The Wombles choose their names from Great Uncle Bulgaria's old atlas. Bungo just closes his eyes and points. 'Silly sort of name' says Great Uncle Bulgaria, 'but it rather suits you.'

The Wombles

Sometimes shy, always adorable, Wombles are kindly furry, brown, rather fat, creatures of fun, mischief, merriment and good works. Their mission in life is to do what they are most famous for – making good use of bad rubbish. They are working, indeed (Orinoco apart) hard-working, Wombles. But the Wombles don't just clear up after us, they also show us what's valuable in life.

REMEMBER YOU'RE A WOMBLE!

The Wombles live in a cosy and warm underground Burrow on Wimbledon Common where Great Uncle Bulgaria has his study, Tobermory his workshop and Madame Cholet her kitchen. The young working Wombles, Tomsk, Bungo, Orinoco and Wellington, all share the same dorm, pretty happily – so long as they don't plan a Midnight Feast and hide the food in greedy Orinoco's bed.

The Burrow is a masterpiece of make-do. Everything
in it is made from, mended by and repaired with
things the Wombles tidy up from Wimbledon
Common. Rubbish, all of it, but not to the
Wombles. Every piece of detritus left on the
Common by those most careless of
creatures, human beings, is collected by
one Womble or another – from the largest
rusty mangle, most immobile ancient
stove, to the tiniest sweet wrapper,
everything is picked up by paw, packed
neatly away in a tidy bag and taken to
Tobermory. Unless the found item is
The Times in which case it goes
directly to Great Uncle Bulgaria,
who regards it as an oracle that
never lies.

Which Womble are you?

The Wombles make up all the elements of a society: Madame Cholet is the heart and soul of the Burrow with her warm heart and fiery temper, Tobermory, the fix-it Womble who never lets you down is its backbone, while the all-wise Great Uncle Bulgaria is its conscience. These three set the tone for the running of the Burrow and within this their younger charges – the bossy joker Bungo, greedy, lazy, self-conscious and adorable Orinoco, shy brilliant Wellington and strong, dependable, sporty Tomsk – can roam wombling free.

There are Wombles all over the world, for as Great Uncle Bulgaria says, 'If it wasn't for us wombles cleaning up behind them, human beings would be knee deep in rubbish by now. Silly sort of creatures, human beings. I'll never understand them. Not if I live to be three hundred. Ho hum.'

Ten things you never knew about the Wombles

 Wombles are one big, happy family. How they procreate is their own business.

 Wombles live to be about 150 years old. This means Great Uncle Bulgaria is certainly still with us.

 Wombles are apolitical. During the 1974 elections all three political parties solicited the Wombles' support, but via their creator Elisabeth Beresford, they refused.

 Six Jesuit priests are permitted to run as Wombles in the London marathon each year – it's for charity.

 Wombles can hold their breath underwater for many minutes at a time.

'Greetings, fellow Wombles and to human beings everywhere! I and my Wombles are flourishing and I hope you are too. Just always remember – Womble up the rubbish and put it in the bin.'

MESSAGE FROM GREAT UNCLE BULGARIA

Wombles so love to talk that being sent to Coventry is one of the worst punishments they can suffer.

 Wombles under stress suffer from 'falling fur' ailment. Orinoco is rather prone to it as waiting for dinnertime often distresses him.

 Prince Charles is a Wombles fan, allegedly the Queen too.

 Tobermory is Elisabeth Beresford's favourite Womble – the ultimate recycling Womble.

 The only Womble not named after a place? – MacWomble the Terrible.

Great Uncle Bulgaria

The Wombles' leader and their conscience.

Great Uncle Bulgaria is as old as the hills and far far wiser. Effortlessly authoritative he commands enormous respect from all the Wombles, a respect which comes not merely from his position in the Burrow, but from the genuine admiration the other Wombles have for him.

The young Wombles think Great Uncle Bulgaria knows everything – sometimes he thinks so too.

Great Uncle Bulgaria keeps his mind active, stimulated daily by reading *The Times* which can always be found for him on the Common by one Womble or another. It is often from the newspaper that he gets the inspiration for one of his big ideas of which he is very fond, rather to Tobermory's alarm.

One windy blustery day an article in *The Times* alerts him to the worldwide threat of pollution and upon reading it he convenes a Wombles meeting and announces a competition for the finest invention to help stamp out pollution. Tobermory wins with the first smell-free, fuel-free clockwork car.

Great Uncle Bulgaria is always sending his Wombles off on adventures and loves hearing news of their exploits, such as their encounter with the Loch Ness Water Womble, Nessie, and MacWomble the Terrible.

Great Uncle Bulgaria's role is not only to think up grand schemes; his leadership skills are also invaluable on a day-to-day basis.

So when the Wombles find instruments on the Common they form a band, but only with Great Uncle Bulgaria conducting is the sound harmonious not cacophonous.

'Good Gracious!' says Great Uncle Bulgaria. 'What a hailstorm and from a clear blue sky!'
'Er, it's actually a golf ball' says Tomsk, and Great Uncle Bulgaria, who loves taking up challenges, happily learns to play golf.

For Great Uncle Bulgaria is a born leader, but a leader who listens to his flock (if you can imagine a flock of Wombles!).

So when the famous Scottish Womble MacWomble the Terrible comes to stay in Wimbledon, Great Uncle Bulgaria comes to the rescue by skilfully engineering their visitor's return to Scotland, so saving them all from endless massed Womble pipe band performances.

Yes, Great Uncle Bulgaria is a considerate Womble. When Tobermory finds that hot weather is making dust overwhelm the study, Great Uncle Bulgaria doesn't blanch at his order that all Wombles dust themselves down.

In his study Great Uncle Bulgaria sneezes, sneezes again, and then sneezes enormously and wonders what is wrong with the Burrow. He goes to find Tobermory in the workshop and encounters a sign on the door:

**No Dusty Wombles
To Be Admitted.
Delicate Repairs Mean
That Every Womble Must
Dust Themselves Off.
P.S THIS MEANS YOU!**

*So Great Uncle Bulgaria
does so – rules are rules.*

Great Uncle Bulgaria is always there for his Wombles, whether that means listening to Tobermory fulminating:

Tobermory is over-tired and the young Wombles' antics are beginning to get to him. He launches into a bit of a rant. Great Uncle Bulgaria sympathises, listens patiently and agrees, because he knows you can't hurry a Womble who has a grievance to get off his chest.

Or giving succour to Orinoco:

Orinoco finds an old vacuum cleaner on the Common and Tobermory and Wellington set to mending it – they think it might be the solution to the dust problem. Orinoco foolishly volunteers to test it. A few alarming seconds later he sadly realises that not only has his fur just been sucked all over, but also that the machine is not going to be given to him to ease his tidying-up duties but is to be used in the Burrow, and on Wombles.

Great Uncle Bulgaria comforts him – he did them all a service and one day it will rain, there won't be dust in the burrow, and maybe he'll be able to use it outside. Orinoco is consoled.

And Great Uncle Bulgaria always brings out the good in others.

One long winter evening Great Uncle Bulgaria tells the story of the Purple Paw Mystery when the Burrow was invaded by a mysterious purple-pawed monster. It turns out to be Tomsk's pawprints from felt tip pens he squashed with his paws. Great Uncle Bulgaria tells the story well, vividly recreating Tobermory calling Tomsk a Great Gormless Womble! But he concludes that the story has taught them two things – that they are safe in the Burrow and that thanks to Tomsk there is an efficient way of getting ink out of old felt tip pens.

Above all else Great Uncle Bulgaria is the Wombles' guiding force – whatever they get up to they always need him.

Great Uncle Bulgaria is superb at dealing
with his Wombles because he knows them
so very well.

*Great Uncle Bulgaria tries to explain a
plan to Tomsk and Wellington. Tomsk is
silent and visibly confused; Wellington is
excited and his mind begins to wander.*

*Great Uncle Bulgaria tells Tomsk that
Wellington will explain it to him later, because
he understands Tomsk's brain, and tells Wellington
to stop day-dreaming because he understands
his brain very well too.*

While Great Uncle Bulgaria does keep up with the times, he also likes to revel in the memories of his comparative youth and indulge his advancing years. So, although he reads *The Times*, he does not always read today's copy – indeed he often re-reads the papers from July 1935, one of his favourite periods.

Great Uncle Bulgaria is a very open-minded Womble but he does enjoy his firm opinions on the subject of the animals of the Common.

'Badgers are alright up to a point, but slow, and have no conversation at all. Otters are as stupid as ducks and you can't get much sillier than that.'
'And squirrels' adds Tomsk.
'Don't start mixing with that riff raff!' replies Uncle Bulgaria.

Great Uncle Bulgaria's life lessons

Value the important things in life
Tomsk once saves the burrow by clinging onto a falling tree and diverting its fall. But Tobermory is torn as to what to attend to first. 'The cracks in the walls!', says Tobermory. 'A Womble is more important than a Burrow,' says Great Uncle Bulgaria to the chastened Tobermory.

A leader suffers for their people, or Wombles
The winter snows are at their worst and the Wombles are running out of food. They are hungry, Great Uncle Bulgaria especially so because known only to Madame Cholet he orders his rations halved. 'You don't need so much at my age,' he says, and pulls his shawl tighter so she won't see his straggled fur.

Admit fault

'Everyone makes mistakes,' says Great Uncle Bulgaria, 'I made one once. Never be ashamed to admit it.'

If a lesson is worth teaching, it's worth teaching well

Alderney goads Bungo into building a snow Great Uncle Bulgaria but building too good a likeness of a Womble is frowned on. It could lead to a great Womble hunt by humans which would only end badly. They go to look at it the next morning.

The fur looks a little melted and the nose a bit squashy says Bungo. Then he gets the most tremendous clout round the ears, and Great Uncle Bulgaria's booming voice greets them as he pelts them with snowballs all the way back to the burrow. 'Ho hum' mutters Great Uncle Bulgaria and snuggles his back paws into his fur-lined boots – 'It's hard on an old Womble's feet being stuck in the snow at eight in the morning.'

 ## Responsibility encourages responsible behaviour

Great Uncle Bulgaria appoints Orinoco his Private Office Womble for the organisation of the midsummer outing. Orinoco makes a little badge with POW on it which he hangs around his neck while he trots up and down the burrow feeling very important. 'Gives him a feeling of responsibility,' says Great Uncle Bulgaria. 'Takes his mind off his stomach too,' he adds, chuckling.

Play people at their own game
Great Uncle Bulgaria snorts at Orinoco's self-serving proverb that 'Too much work and not enough rest stops a Womble from feeling his best,' and instead tells him that 'Too much food and no work makes a fat Womble shirk!'

Trust your instincts

The Wombles are longing for rain in the dusty hot summer. In the middle of the night Great Uncle Bulgaria demands that the door be opened. 'Now?' queries Tomsk, nightwatch Womble. Great Uncle Bulgaria steps out, greets a surprised badger, and senses the rain coming in the pricking of his fur.

Everyone needs pampering sometimes

Tomsk has disappeared. Great Uncle Bulgaria is so worried that he doesn't even drink a cup of Madame Cholet's recuperative hot acorn juice. Tobermory comes into his study and insists Great Uncle Bulgaria rests. For once, Great Uncle Bulgaria allows himself to be bossed about, and meekly does as he's told. Tomsk had been carried away down an old water pipe but even while the old Wombles are talking, a swan, that Tomsk saved from drowning, finds and rescues him.

To be calm is to be in charge
Great Uncle Bulgaria returns to the Burrow and finds everyone all of a jitter. Great Uncle Bulgaria alone is calm. And, astonishingly, the moment he re-enters the Burrow all the rushing about and the shouting and the panic vanishes.

Orinoco

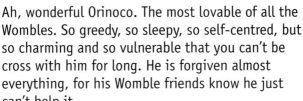

**Fat, quick-thinking,
lazy, lovable.
A Womble of paradoxes.**

Ah, wonderful Orinoco. The most lovable of all the
Wombles. So greedy, so sleepy, so self-centred, but
so charming and so vulnerable that you can't be
cross with him for long. He is forgiven almost
everything, for his Womble friends know he just
can't help it.

For Orinoco, every moment of every day is either a potential snooze or snack but these very interests often lead him to unexpected discoveries– it is amazing the number of things Orinoco finds through trying to sleep on them or hoping to eat them.

He sees something hidden in the snow and, thinking it is a snow cake, he delves inside and comes up with a sledge.

Once, in putting up his paw to ask for an extra bun he found he had inadvertently volunteered for an adventure around the world in a hot air balloon.

All the Wombles love food, as Madame Cholet knows only too well, but Orinoco really has a deep passion for all things culinary. He dreams not only of food, but of Madame Cholet's finest dishes, and he spends his leisure time reading such tomes as the chocolate catalogue from 'Fortune and Bason's'.

From time to time he tries to impart what he believes to be his expert knowledge to Madame Cholet, but that's a step too far. He can't actually cook and he's far too lazy for kitchen work where Madame Cholet's eyes are always on him. Tidying up the Common may be hard work on a somewhat overweight Womble but there he can always find a nearby bush to hide behind and savour 40 winks.

Paradoxically, although Orinoco is extremely lazy, it is precisely this quality that makes him very quick-witted when he suddenly finds himself in a fix. For when you spend so much of the day in rapturous dreams of food or sleep, problems have to be solved in double quick time.

REMEMBER · YOU'RE A WOMBLE

One winter's day Madame Cholet is making dinner, singing happily to herself, until she realises they have run out of moss. She informs Great Uncle Bulgaria who is alarmed indeed; he is sure there will be a solution but right now he has to judge the snow Womble competition.

While the other Wombles set to crafting their snow Womble, Orinoco rolls one tiny ball of snow, then declares he needs a rest after all that hard work and so saying falls off a log backwards to sleep.

Great Uncle Bulgaria judges each snow Womble in turn and finally reaches Orinoco – who has just woken up to find that his one snowball collapses in his hands. Suddenly he needs a snow Womble very fast.

He stands up the log he slept on and turns it so that a branch jutting out creates a Womble nose and then puts his own hat on it – it really does look rather like a Womble. Great Uncle Bulgaria finds it very good indeed. At this point Madame Cholet appears and congratulates Monsieur Bulgaria for being so clever – the log is covered with moss! Great Uncle Bulgaria declares Bungo the winner of the competition and with Orinoco's moss they shall all have delicious moss pie for dinner.

Orinoco muses whether he will be allowed a second helping for finding the moss.

Orinoco is also splendidly inventive when it comes to working out how to get things he wants, from the netting he finds on the Common which he turns into a fairly serviceable hammock – unfortunately rather vulnerable to breezes –

to the tale of the Vanishing Pancake.

Delicious smells permeate the burrow, Orinoco is helping Madame Cholet make pancakes.
'Hmm, needs more dandelion salt, don't you think?' says Orinoco.
'Are you trying to teach me how to cook? Me, a Womble cordon bleu!' Madame Cholet exclaims.

*Orinoco swiftly backtracks and
apologises. He then tosses the
pancake into the air but it
thwacks Tobermory on the nose
just as he is walking into the
kitchen. Madame Cholet is
appalled and chases Orinoco
from the room. Tobermory
has a better plan – he brings
Madame Cholet a bunch of daffodils and praises her
excellent cooking.*

*Sitting out on the Common above ground, Orinoco is
somewhat resentful. 'I was only trying to help, I am
probably the best judge of pancakes in the world as
it happens, actually.' Back in the kitchen Tobermory
wins Madame Cholet's admiration for being strong
enough to hold the pan with only one paw and he
tosses the pancake. Sadly for him he never sees it
again. Orinoco is sitting above the chimney exit and,
seeing his chance, attaches a hook to a string and
snags it up the chimney.*

*'Nothing fancy, but very nice. It travels well, both
upwards and, hrr hrr, downwards.' says Orinoco
gobbling it up.*

But although Orinoco loves to play jokes on others and is forever dressing up in clothes too big for him or riding joke bicycles too small for him, he is terribly prone to falling for practical jokes played on him.

Orinoco has the idea of planting bulbs on the Common near the burrow to grow lovely daffodils. But Wellington and Tobermory connect up an electric light bulb on the ground to trick him into believing they can grow electricity. From Orinoco's point of view it backfires dreadfully – he couldn't care less whether or not they can grow electricity, but he does see that with light on the Common he'll be expected to start tidying up even earlier in the day.

'From now on' he says, 'I'll keep my bright ideas dark.'

Another time, Wellington convinces Orinoco that he's invisible which Orinoco is happy to believe – it only becomes a problem when he realises he might miss dinner as a result.

Bungo and Wellington are off to work. And here's Orinoco, late as usual. He trips over the step – 'Did you ever see such a poor Womble?' he says. 'Falling fur, tired paws, and I can hardly keep my eyes open. And why? Because I'm overworked!' he cries exasperatedly and then kicks a tin and gets caught up in a net.

He calls out to Wellington who is passing, but Wellington thinks Orinoco is malingering and needs a good practical joke to restore his humour and so pretends he can't see or hear Orinoco. Orinoco is amazed and delighted at this change of fortunes – he concludes he must be invisible and if he is, he might as well sit back and enjoy 40 winks.

All is well until Great Uncle Bulgaria calls dinner time and watches Orinoco vainly try to free himself from the net before extracting a promise from Orinoco not to become invisible again.

Although Orinoco himself does nothing at any kind of pace, he is impatient – so when he decides to grow a marrow he demands instant results.

But sadly he is also the kind of Womble for whom plans often start out well but end badly.

Orinoco decides to help his marrow along with some Wizz plant food he finds. The instructions on the packet can't be right he is sure. 'This marrow must need more than a teaspoonful, it's dying of hunger.' So he pours out the whole contents. Rather to his surprise it does have the desired effect – the marrow grows almost to the size of a Womble overnight. Orinoco is amazed and even slightly alarmed. 'Don't strain yourself, marrow' he tells it.

But now the marrow is so huge that he and Tobermory struggle to pick it up. They grapple with it, lose their grip, and it describes a beautiful marrow parabola before descending, undignified, to earth, splitting into hundreds of squidgy pieces. 'What a way for a marrow to go!' says Tobermory, and tells Orinoco to look on the bright side – they'll have marrow seeds a plenty.

But Orinoco wanders off to supper, quite put off horticulture.

Orinoco is awfully selfish – he once consumed an entire picnic made for all of them.

'Well, the basket used to be heavy' said Orinoco, 'but then I used my head.'
'You've eaten the lot!' exclaims Tomsk.
'No I haven't,' says Orinoco truthfully, diving into the basket and pulling out a biscuit from one corner, then eating it.

And the Wombles' plan for a midnight feast, which involves hiding food in Orinoco's bed, goes similarly awry. But still the others are not cross with him – it's just the way he is and if they don't want him to whip all the food then they shouldn't put temptation in front of him as he just cannot resist it. He has the stomach for a lot of things, but never for that.

But he is lovable despite his selfishness because he is so self-conscious

54

about being fat, lazy, stupid and generally standing out. Endearingly, he is forever taking on fitness binges when his fatness gets to him.

When Tomsk hauls in a huge grandfather clock from the Common Tobermory is delighted. It won't keep time, but he will turn it into a weighing machine. 'Isn't that right, Podgy?' he questions Orinoco.

Orinoco is shocked into weighing himself – ten past three. That does sound a bit much. So he goes for a walk to bring the pounds off and weighs himself again – twenty past four. He's gaining weight! Some quick physical jerks – now he's half past five! Finally Tobermory puts him out of his misery – he hopes Orinoco hasn't been weighing himself on the machine, because it's not working yet. Oh yes, says Orinoco, he knew that.

But though the other Wombles may tease him for being the lazy plump hypochondriac he is, they all love him dearly. Bungo is his closest friend – they both approach life with a similar insouciance. But more often than not, Orinoco just makes his own way through life, drifting through it in a happy daze pondering his next or last snooze or snack.

A carefree, contented and rich life.

Orinoco's life lessons

A joker may not be thick-skinned

It is exactly because Orinoco is prepared to make himself look stupid that he is the most entertaining Womble, often ribbing the others and playing practical jokes. But he is at heart a very sensitive soul and the others respect that.

Hard work is its own reward (but a dandelion omelette helps too)

There was once, just once, when Orinoco worked really hard on something. He cleaned, mended and polished a new cooker for Madame Cholet. Then, with a final touch of brilliance, he used the excess acorn grains in acorn juice to create a filter to soak up cooking smells. He felt justly proud of himself, but was even more pleased with Madame Cholet's dandelion omelette and curried sycamore leaves for supper.

Everybody must take charge some time

When Orinoco and Bungo fly to America in a hot air balloon, Bungo is always steering, directing, taking the lead. But at one point as they drift across the ocean, Orinoco sees that Bungo is looking tired and homesick. Suddenly he orders in a voice like Great Uncle Bulgaria's that Bungo take a nap, and he takes over flying and steering while Bungo snoozes. And that is not all, for when the fog comes down he brooks no opposition but barks orders about face masks and seat belts, taking charge and saving them both.

Hold on to your temper

The balloon successfully crosses the ocean and they set down on land, waiting for their American cousin Yellowstone who is due to meet them, until Bungo admits that Yellowstone probably won't be along soon because he forgot to reset the compass. He did try to tell Orinoco but...Orinoco takes a deep breath and counts up to ten, then twenty, then fifty. Orinoco calls Bungo a stupid Womble but says that what can't be put right makes a Womble sit tight and they had better stay there, wherever there is.

Don't ask for forgiveness, earn it

One winter the Common freezes in a deep lasting frost. While the young Wombles frolic in the snow the older Wombles know this is no game. Snow and ice means not only no litter to clear, but no food. They are down to their last 10 days of rations and praying for a thaw when Orinoco finds a crate stuffed full of bread, cakes and buns. Without thinking of his near starving friends he falls on them. A wicked Womble sin under any circumstances – not to share – but at such a time? Shamed by Tobermory who catches him red-handed and disgusted at himself he leaves the Burrow determined to find more food to save his friends.

Thanks to Great Uncle Bulgaria's clever thinking Bungo finds Orinoco at 'Fortune and Bason's', rifling through the rubbish bins and finding chocolate loot. They return to the Burrow to be happily reunited with their friends and Orinoco is forgiven by all.

Madame Cholet

**Kind, motherly, bossy, fiery.
A Womble to stay on the right side of.**

Madame Cholet – the world-famous *cordon bleu* chef who rules the Wombles' kitchen and their hearts.

There is nothing so comforting to a tired, frightened or troubled Womble as a cup of Madame Cholet's marvellous hot buttercup broth, given with a kindly smile and a gentle *'Tiens'.* But make no mistake, Madame Cholet is no pushover – she rules her kitchen absolutely, knows her due and will not put up with any less.

In the kitchen Madame Cholet is berating Tobermory. A blockage in the ventilation shaft is making her kitchen smell awful – how can she work in such a kitchen? How can she work with one paw held over her nose?

Tobermory must do something and do something now! Tobermory tries to calm her, Tomsk has gone to fetch a pipe cleaner, it'll soon be mended. But that is not enough for Madame Cholet, she cannot take it, she exclaims in her Franglais. She is going! Yes certainly she is leaving! pausing only to tell Tomsk, ze stupide Womble, to get out of her way.

The ventilation shaft is cleared in double quick time.

Madame Cholet is expert at getting what she wants from the Wombles – she even puts the incorrigible Orinoco to work and won't put up with any of his slacking.

Orinoco persuades Madame Cholet to let him work in the kitchen but she won't let him near the prepared food – it's just cutting grass, chopping nettles, topping and tailing berries. It's even harder work than out on the Common because Madame Cholet seems to have eyes in the back of her head and always gets him working on another job when he's finished the first. After a little while Madame Cholet gives him an affectionate cuff and a bar of chocolate and sends him back to Tobermory.

Bossy yet gentle Madame Cholet is the spiritual heart of the Burrow who knows what she's about. There is no brooking argument with her – when she puts her paw down, it stays down. All the Wombles are careful to keep on the good side of Madame Cholet.

Even for Great Uncle Bulgaria there are times when what Madame Cholet says, goes.

Madame Cholet is picking daffodils happily – it's the first day of spring and time for the Burrow to be spring cleaned. Oh how she loves it! Great Uncle Bulgaria is snoring dreamily, he hasn't remembered

the day's significance. The phone rings, he starts awake and declares he's very busy, very tied-up, but Tobermory is not shaken by this obvious bluster, he just calmly warns Great Uncle Bulgaria that it's spring cleaning time. They commiserate with each other about the inevitable dust up the nose, but nothing can be done. Tobermory looks at the long list of things Madame Cholet has given him to do and sighs.

Meeting Madame Cholet's wrath is certainly not a happy experience:

Bungo appears and sees Tobermory wiping sweat from his brow – you'd be hot if you'd just come out of the kitchen and been scorched by Madame Cholet's tongue.

And they are all wary of her tendency to be an emotional powderkeg.

The young Wombles are horrified when an innocent game of conkers ends up smashing Madame Cholet's necklace.

They immediately start working on a solution though, and she is delighted with Wellington's idea of making a new necklace from tiny baked and painted conkers.

But it takes only a little flattery and attention and Madame Cholet melts as easily as her buttercup ice-cream.

Tobermory brings Madame Cholet a bunch of daffodils. 'Ooh, Monsieur Tobermory' she simpers.

And she is the most kind-hearted of all the Wombles (by nature a very kind-hearted lot). Her emotional care for the Wombles is part of what holds them together.

On a professional level, Madame Cholet is highly concerned about her good reputation. Fortunately, she is world-renowned – from Germany to America and Australia to Japan, adventuring Wombles are always asked how their famous Madame Cholet is doing and whether they perchance might know any of her finest recipes? This does, Madame Cholet would have to admit, please her greatly.

REMEMBER · YOU'RE A WOMBLE

But it is not just for show – she wants to *be* a good cook, not just have the reputation of one.

Madame Cholet tastes the bitter leaves Cousin Botany has grown underwater and grimaces a little. But here is a challenge! To make these acrid plants taste good is what a real cook should do.

Madame Cholet espouses a marvellous form of Womble logic. She chose a French name because she is a cook, and then she speaks French from time to time, because she has a French name.

Madame Cholet is highly valued by all the Wombles she cares for. Although she works behind the scenes, everyone knows they need her, and if they ever forget, it doesn't take much to remind them.

FLOUR

Everyone is shirking blackberry picking duties. Madame Cholet declares it is too much that she has to do everything herself and flounces out of the kitchen.

The Wombles believe she has gone for good and the alarm goes between Tobermory and Great Uncle Bulgaria. What shall they do? Their attempt at cooking is not good – 'How is the soup?' asks Great Uncle Bulgaria. 'Terrible,' says Tobermory. 'And that's only for starters,' puts in Bungo. 'What about nexts?' Madame Cholet returns to find a kitchen full of eager volunteers.

When Madame Cholet takes charge of the burrow in
Great Uncle Bulgaria and Tobermory's absence there
is no problem at all, just as Great Uncle Bulgaria
foresees as he tells her of their departure.

*'I see' says Madame Cholet to Great Uncle Bulgaria,
'Don't give it another thought. They know that I am
the one who gets their meals, and, Wombles being
Wombles, and very fond of their stomachs, they'll do
exactly as I say, do not doubt it, Bulgaria.'*
'I don't,' says Great Uncle Bulgaria, and chuckles.

Of course should a Womble fail to
appreciate the food they eat,
Madame Cholet is not only worried
for them, shocked indeed, but
also deeply hurt and she mutters
all sorts of French under her
breath that the Wombles in
turn are rather shocked to hear.

*Tobermory and Orinoco work
so hard on mending, cleaning
and polishing the old stove that
they actually miss supper.
And it is Madame Cholet's*

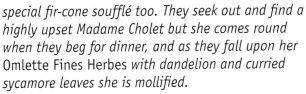

special fir-cone soufflé too. They seek out and find a highly upset Madame Cholet but she comes round when they beg for dinner, and as they fall upon her Omlette Fines Herbes with dandelion and curried sycamore leaves she is mollified.

Yes, food is Madame Cholet's craft and through food she expresses her love and warmth for the Wombles, as well as a superb creativity.

DELICIOUS MADAME CHOLET MENUS
(for Wombles)

Extra-specially delicious casserole with fried brambles
and dandelions, a touch of moss-garlic, sliced oak
apples, a pinch of elmbark and a bubbling crust of
toadstools all golden brown. Followed by double
daisy ice-cream and a spoonful of clover cream.

Acorn and bramble stew accompanied by grass buns
with acorn spread. Daisy ice-cream with
hot bubbly buttercup sauce.

Dandelion and bark pie, with a touch of moss garlic,
followed by oak-apple jelly with buttercup ice-cream.

Queen's Mere Weed Spread on grass toast,
followed by apple, orange and banana stew
and with daisy ice-cream for afters.

Bramble and bracken pie followed by
buttercup roly poly with daisy cream.

Baked bracken on
grass toast.
Nettle pudding and
daisy custard.

WOMBLE SNACKS

Acorn pasties with oak-leaf gravy, toadstool
scramble on fried moss bread, Bracken toast with
fried nettles, bracken marmalade and dandelion
toast with a few fresh hazelnuts for afters.

A PICNIC LUNCH

Banana skin biscuits, orange peel buns
with a pinch of sweet moss and lemon peel
topping, grass bread sandwiches filled with creamy
toadstool spread, and a Womble delicacy,
chilled eggshell consommé.

One of Madame Cholet's greatest triumphs was a
whole bag of bananas (Orinoco had procured them
by tracking picnicking human beings from one side
of the Common to the other) rolled and coated in
grass seed dough, baked very slowly and served
with thick, creamy rowan berry sauce.

America

Daisy cream with hot grass sauce,
Bracken buns and clover spread, Redwood
triple-decker sandwiches, Toadstool takeaways,
Moss crackers, Acorn chocolate-covered pancakes
with whipped daisy cream, Waffles with clover
syrup, Nutties loaded with cream, Blueberry
pudding and bracken batter cakes.

Germany

Mugs of acorn juice topped with daisy cream.
Special fir-cone and moss strudel.

Tibet
Yellow-flower tea and lichen cakes.

Australia
Thorn juice, and blue gum waffles.

New Zealand
Rotorua moss casserole, and Wanaker
water-weed cream ices.

Madame Cholet's life lessons

Everyone's work has value

Whenever the Wombles neglect to look out for Madame Cholet by not helping in the kitchen or failing to bring in supplies from the Common, just one blast of that fiery temper and they soon enough realise that they can't do without her.

Don't underestimate the power behind the throne

Madame Cholet doesn't appear to hold much sway over the affairs of the burrow, but if she ever wants anything, it's hers for the taking.

There are many ways to make a view heard

Madame Cholet gives a loud sniff to show what she thinks of the idea of Tobermory needing all the stray cutlery collected from the Common this week and none of it staying in her kitchen.

Love is having an advantage and not pressing it home

The Wombles love their food and are especially devoted to Madame Cholet's creations so she has them over a barrel and they all know it. Even Great Uncle Bulgaria. But of course, being such a good kind Womble, Madame Cholet never pushes her advantage and so she is universally loved.

Wellington

The brilliant absent-minded inventor.

Clever, shy, dreamy Wellington always has his head in a book and his mind a world away.

A small, charming, helpful and very polite Womble, Wellington sees the best in others, tending to put himself down in comparison. As Wellington sees it, he is not dashing and brave like Bungo, or strong like Tomsk, or sure of himself like Orinoco. But of course while Wellington is self-effacing and exceptionally modest, he is also a genius inventor, as all the Wombles know. And somewhere inside him, Wellington knows it too.

Wellington is not an odd job man like Tobermory but a Womble of real brain power. His cleverness is legendary among the Wombles and they often assume he will somehow be able to solve almost any problem. He certainly has made some highly impressive inventions, from his most ambitious – a solution which dissolves plastic – to his most useful – the inter-burrow telephone exchange:

It has been a very windy night and there is rubbish strewn everywhere on the Common. Great Uncle Bulgaria announces that he doesn't want any Womble to get lost and looks pointedly over his spectacles at Wellington who has no sense of direction and is so very dreamy. 'Sorry' says Wellington. Great Uncle Bulgaria says that he doesn't have anything to apologise for, yet. Just keep in touch, says Great Uncle Bulgaria. Tomsk and Bungo start clearing up, Orinoco slopes off for a snooze, and Wellington ponders how they are meant to keep in touch.

Off wanders Wellington, muttering to himself, when he comes upon a tin can and string. By chance Bungo finds the other end and they both pull. Being Wombles of a tenacious nature they don't let go until they bump into each other. Seeing the can and string and remembering Great Uncle Bulgaria's words Wellington says he has an Idea and asks Bungo if he'd like to take part in an Experiment. 'Not particularly,' says Bungo, 'Will it blow up?' he asks. Wellington says that he thinks not, then that he is sure not. Bungo reluctantly agrees. Wellington attaches a can to the other end of the string and they stand at a distance. Wellington speaks into the can.

'Wellington calling – peep peep!' Bungo practically falls over with surprise as this greeting reaches him loud and clear through his tin can.

He pats Wellington affectionately on the back 'Bungo calling Wellington awfully clever! You've invented the first Womble keep in touch telephone system.'

REMEMBER · YOU'RE A WOMBLE ·

They arrive at the burrow and Wellington shows
Great Uncle Bulgaria the invention by putting the
can next to dozing Orinoco's ear and inviting Great
Uncle Bulgaria to bellow down the line to wake him
up. Orinoco leaps up at the loud noise and they are
all highly impressed and congratulate Wellington.
Extra supper helpings for him tonight!

Wellington's system is installed in the Burrow with
a telephone exchange at its centre to connect all
the different rooms to each other. Welllington
often mans the exchange,
but it is Tobermory who
sets it up. As is so often
the case, Wellington
has an idea and
then Tobermory
sees it through.

Tobermory always calls on Wellington to help out with any project of his and in return Wellington willingly lends a paw whether it's ideas that Tobermory wants or a good old-fashioned workshop assistant. They make an excellent, very complementary team, producing results that use Tobermory's technological and fix-it know-how and Wellington's far-sighted inventive thinking – like the Wombles' clockwork car, Womble 1.

Wellington is not just a thinking Womble but a thoughtful one too. He looks out for his friends and knows what's good for them – whether it's playing a practical joke on Orinoco to restore that fat Womble's spirits or not bothering Tomsk with details. Wellington gets on well with everyone although he has a particular affinity, the affinity of opposites, with Tomsk.

'Now do you understand?' asks Wellington. There is a longish pause. 'No' says Tomsk regretfully. 'Never mind,' says Wellington. 'I'll start the machine.'

Tomsk is a big fan of Wellington's because he admires his cleverness so much. Once, Wellington reads a small tract on oil rigs and concludes he can drill for oil in the pond on Wimbledon Common. The episode does not end particularly successfully but Tomsk supports him all the way:

Wellington plans to copy the picture of an oil rig he has found. The raw materials they have are not ideal and neither Wellington nor Tomsk are good with their paws so it is time-consuming and painful on the knuckles. But Tomsk isn't worried; he thinks Wellington is the cleverest of all the Wombles and can do anything, so he just waits to be told what to do next.

But although Wellington may invent something brilliant, his dreaminess means he sometimes forgets a crucial component along the way.

Hearing Great Uncle Bulgaria reminisce about the vintage days of steam trains sets Wellington thinking. When he comes across some old pram wheels on  the Common and Tomsk rolls by in a barrel there's nothing for it but to turn them into a train – the *Flying Womble*! They all clambour aboard, the train zooms fast downhill and as Great Uncle Bulgaria is concluding that his re-reading the old timetable in his study is even bringing the sights and sounds back to him, all the Wombles are having a high old time. Until Wellington remembers he forgot the brakes. The train crashes into the Burrow door just as the supper bell rings.

Bang on time!

Wellington is not brave, but he can steel himself for adventure and really rather likes it when he does. So when Great Uncle Bulgaria has the idea of the Wombles circumnavigating the globe in two hot air balloons, Wellington is more than happy to set off on the voyage with Tomsk. His inventions continue abroad: he gives the Yeti Wombles a suggestion about how to hide their tracks from humans – the last Yeti in a line could drape a shawl around their shoulders with a rake attached to the bottom which would erase the telltale back-paw prints.

Wellington likes to have helpful ideas, but he's also happy just to be helpful – he is one of the first to volunteer for blackberry picking.

· REMEMBER ·
YOU'RE A WOMBLE

Wellington is a great admirer of Orinoco's fearlessness but he especially likes the way that Orinoco sparks off ideas in Wellington's head. He has the idea for an abacus after hearing Orinoco declare that his conker is worth ten of Bungo's.

Wellington can take what other Wombles say literally, often with marvellous results.

Orinoco is feeling rather sorry for himself – he is tired, over-worked and almost wasting away from lack of food. He ambles into the library and stumbles upon Wellington. He bursts out that he might just vanish quite away! Wellington is amazed and wants to know exactly how.

Wellington takes minutes Womble-style:

Great Uncle Bulgaria announces that Orinoco should be sent on an expedition. 'It's high time he started pulling his weight – and he's got plenty of that all right.' There is a snuffling sound which means Great Uncle Bulgaria is enjoying a small joke and Wellington writes in brackets (laugh, laugh, laugh).

Like all shy creatures Wellington is deeply self-conscious, but being Wellington he has his own solutions to embarrassing moments.

Bungo is stuck up a tree after reaching for a particularly inaccessible piece of rubbish. It takes a super effort of Wombles teamwork to bring him down. 'Don't worry,' calls out Wellington, 'Tobermory will know how.' Tobermory emerges from the burrow. 'Hmm, getting Wombles out of trees, yes, perfectly simple.' He consults a book and says that what's needed is a leaning tower of Wombles – Tomsk at the bottom because he's the strongest, then Orinoco because he's the fattest.

'I'm not fat, I'm cuddly,' says Orinoco, sending Wellington up before him.

The tower collapses 'Don't drop me, I'll break!'
protests Orinoco.
Then, to his surprise, 'Oh, I bounced.'

*Tobermory tuts as the Womble tower falls to the
ground. What will Great Uncle Bulgaria say? He
consults the book again and decides he needs a rope
lift. He calls out to Wellington to fetch a rope and
throw it up to Bungo who then lowers it. All is going
well, until Madame Cholet appears and calls the
Wombles in for dinner – announcing the menu.
They all rush off but as Bungo comes to earth,
the rope lift sends Wellington hurtling up the
tree. Tobermory thinks they are one
short, but as Bungo steps in he
concludes that all is well.*

*'Oh dear,' says Wellington,
reconciled to his fate.
'If anyone asks I
shall say I'm
bird watching.'*

Wellington's life lessons

REMEMBER · YOU'RE A WOMBLE

Give your thoughts freedom
Tomsk finds Wellington amidst an array of plastic buckets and noxious-smelling liquids.
'What are you doing?' he asks
'Inventing,' says Wellington.
'Inventing what?'
'I shan't know till I've invented it, shall I?'
'No, I suppose not.'

Look after others
Wellington and Tomsk are flying high above the Black Forest in Germany in a hot air balloon, and Tomsk is getting itchy feet. He doesn't say anything, but Wellington can see that he needs to stretch his paws. He decides to be reckless and try to land. They land well and it works out perfectly as they encounter two German Wombles and are fed with

delicious moss strudel and treated to a leather-bound volume of the history of these Wombles which turns out to be written by none other than the great Womble historian, Hapsburg Von Hohenzollern Womble.

Don't typecast
The Wombles are gliding more or less adeptly across the ice which has formed on Queen's Mere pond on the Common. Wellington brakes athletically which surprises Bungo – he does it just to show Bungo he doesn't know as much as he thinks he does.

A character of contradictions is natural
Madame Cholet hears strange sounds in the burrow – could it be haunted? 'As a scientist,' says Wellington 'I don't believe in ghosts. But as a Womble I jolly well do.'

Comparisons are odious, but useful

One day Wellington rescues a young Womble who strays too close to a human being. Wellington looks at the young Womble – *he'd* always been the smallest Womble, but now he suddenly felt quite large and important. It was a new feeling and he liked it.

Responsibility begets self-confidence

Great Uncle Bulgaria goes to the library and finds Wellington quietly reading. Wellington is overawed by Great Uncle Bulgaria's sudden arrival and asks if he should leave, but Great Uncle Bulgaria says that in fact he will need him and wants to entrust him with a secret. Wellington feels more important than ever in his life and draws himself up straight.

Tobermory

The DIY Womble *extraordinaire*. The backbone of the Burrow who gets things done.

Tobermory is not much given to grand schemes (that is Great Uncle Bulgaria's department) but if you have an idea and you need someone to carry it out, Tobermory is your Womble. Supremely practical, Tobermory's genius is in solving problems, and he is good with his paws in exactly the way that Wellington is not.

More than any other Womble Tobermory epitomises their raison d'être – he makes such good use of bad rubbish.

Orinoco hauls an old broken vacuum cleaner into the burrow. Tobermory is delighted, and goes off with it muttering and thinking. He is, as Great Uncle Bulgaria says, a real crafts-Womble – often the things he puts back together work better than they ever did before.

Always happy to help out with any project even if he is sceptical about its aims, Tobermory is the Womble you need when you have a plan because he can follow through an idea like nobody else.

Tobermory is second in command in the Burrow and Great Uncle Bulgaria frequently delegates to him. Tobermory is happy to take on the role but he is always glad to see Great Uncle Bulgaria back. He certainly has no aspirations of leadership for himself.

Indeed once when Great Uncle Bulgaria seemed to be losing the impetus for action Tobermory responded by saying that if he wants to retire they should begin preparing for someone else to take over. That shakes Great Uncle Bulgaria out of his lethargy.

'Now, you young Wombles. Get Wombling!'
says Tobermory.

Tobermory knows how to get the best from others and is a fine task master for the young Wombles.

One day Tobermory falls into a hole in the burrow floor and after Great Uncle Bulgaria opens the door to his study and inadvertently joins him, they agree that the floor must be re-laid with concrete. Great Uncle Bulgaria drums up Womble volunteers. Tobermory sets Tomsk to pickaxing the floor – he knows there's no need to explain to him why. But with Orinoco he has to be more sneaky.

Tobermory finds Orinoco in the kitchen stirring a cup of tea – so therapeutic he says. Tobermory is pleased Orinoco likes it and says he has something much bigger for him to stir. He takes him outside to the cement mixer and explains that Orinoco's job is to make sure the cement is kept on the move by turning the handle, otherwise it will all stick together. But he's not to think he can slack off – Tobermory shows Orinoco a bell he has attached to the handle and tied a long piece of string to, which will keep ringing while Orinoco turns the handle. If it doesn't ring, Tobermory will know Orinoco has stopped turning the handle, then he'll pull on the string, make the bell ring and wake Orinoco up.

Orinoco, incidentally, doesn't resent this close management – he just works within its constraints, ie takes 40 winks when he can't resist it any longer and accepts that he has to wake up again when the bell rings in his ear.

Tobermory is also good at creating a team for a task.

'How do you get on with Tomsk?' asks Tobermory.
'Very well' says Wellington, puzzled. 'I can do things he can't and he can do things I can't.'
'Exactly,' says Tobermory.

But he is not a natural leader and sometimes focuses too much on the process of a task to notice he has not carried his people, or rather his Wombles, with him.

Wellington is operating the interburrow telephone exchange. Great Uncle Bulgaria wants to use it but can only hear drips of water, so he asks to be put through to the workshop straight away. The phone rings in Tobermory's workshop but water runs through the earpiece 'Ooh, straight down the hooter,' says Tobermory.

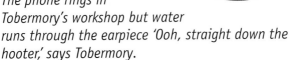

Tobermory phones the dormitory for help in fixing the problem. Tomsk answers and Tobermory gives him fast and furious instructions about disconnecting one pipe, re-connecting another and so forth. Tomsk becomes quite lost and by mistake joins the water pipes to the telephone pipes. He only realises what he has done when he goes to wash his dirty paws. Out of the pipe comes not water but Tobermory's voice 'You silly young womble, just wait until I get my paws on you!'

'Hot and cold running Tobermory, that's what I've got' says Tomsk grinning ruefully.

But for all his bluffness and gruffness Tobermory is excessively fond of the young Wombles and protective of them too.

The circus comes to town! Bungo introduces the fearless bareback rider, Orinoco. Orinoco appears with other cowboy accoutrements to match his hat, and a tiny tricycle, and makes a menace of himself – shooting off in all directions and crashing into things. 'I knew he'd come a cropper' says Tobermory, adding 'I hope he hasn't hurt himself' beneath his breath.

In fact Tobermory is protective of all the Wombles, Great Uncle Bulgaria included, whom he often tries to hold back from doing risky or dangerous things, not that Great Uncle Bulgaria will be persuaded from his duty. If Great Uncle Bulgaria is the Wombles' head of state, held in some awe, always to be obeyed, Tobermory is their father. Strong, always finding a solution to a problem, always willing to help, seemingly invincible, never showing any doubt and enduringly protective.

TOBERMORY'S FINEST INVENTIONS

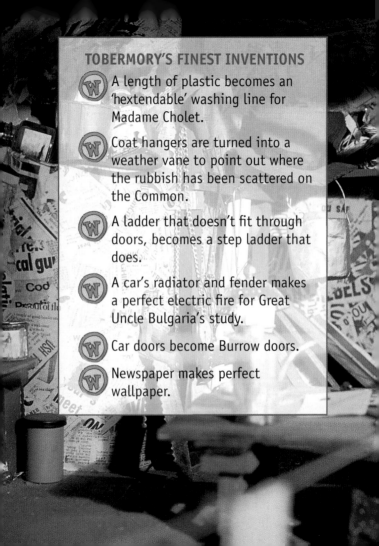

A length of plastic becomes an 'hextendable' washing line for Madame Cholet.

Coat hangers are turned into a weather vane to point out where the rubbish has been scattered on the Common.

A ladder that doesn't fit through doors, becomes a step ladder that does.

A car's radiator and fender makes a perfect electric fire for Great Uncle Bulgaria's study.

Car doors become Burrow doors.

Newspaper makes perfect wallpaper.

Tobermory's life lessons

Be happy with who you are
Wellington is an intellectual
Womble whereas Tobermory is good
with his paws. His great skill is in mending and
fixing, not inventing. But Tobermory is happy with
who he is and what he has and is not at all jealous
of Wellington and his next generation spirit.

Don't make a fuss, make do
Tobermory is a master of making do, from every
item of Womble furniture to every activity. When it
comes to swimming instructions, the middle pages
of Tobermory's book are missing so it goes
straight from simple life saving to advanced
diving, but as Tobermory says, Wombles
can't be choosers.

Everyone has their faults
When Yellowstone Womble returns to America
Tobermory returns to his normal self – no one had
quite noticed, but Yellowstone put his nose a little
out of joint. (It's just that his ideas for a deep
freeze and an efficiency scheme were rather too
good.)

Being supportive breeds loyalty
Tobermory is mentor to Wellington – advising him
on ideas and encouraging him with his inventions.
As a result, Wellington is
unquestioningly loyal
on Tobermory's
projects.

Let others make their own way

Tobermory discovers the young Wombles secretly constructing something, but he doesn't comment that they should change this bit here and that bit there, because he doesn't want to hurt their feelings – although he makes sure to calculate that no harm should come to them with the current design.

Take your time

Cousin Botany drags Wellington and Tomsk to Tobermory after finding them inadvertently digging up his underwater plant experiments – 'Do with them as you will, you're in charge' he cries, 'if it were me I would send them to Coventry for three months!'

How Botany had turned from a thoughtful quiet Womble to an excitable angry Womble, Tobermory doesn't know. He also doesn't know how to deal with the situation – how he wishes Great Uncle Bulgaria were there. So he takes a deep breath, orders hot drinks, and says that when they arrive they will all talk about this slowly. It was like being in the presence of Great Uncle Bulgaria.

Bungo

Bossy, self-important, bold Bungo.
The fast-track Womble.

Bungo is a young Womble with a great deal of bounce. He orders the others around a bit, and does have a somewhat exaggerated opinion of himself –

Bungo always knows best, according to Bungo.
But he is always willing to get involved, to
volunteer for danger, to try things out.

He is a Womble full of insatiable curiosity who
takes up challenges. Though the others may find
him tiresomely full of himself, they wouldn't be
without him.

*Bungo has been away from the Burrow a while now.
'He's a bossy Womble,' says Orinoco, 'but one
does miss him after a bit.'
'Yes,' Wellington agrees emphatically.*

All Wombles choose their name from Great Uncle Bulgaria's old atlas, stuck together with sticky tape (and with Tobermory's fur which has stuck to the tape). They choose a name when they are old enough and sensible enough to be allowed out to work on the Common – before they have a name they are all just called young Womble. In typical Bungo style, Bungo gets his name by pointing at the map and hoping for the best. 'Silly sort of name' says Great Uncle Bulgaria, 'but it rather suits you.'

Bungo is Orinoco's best friend although neither would ever admit it. As a young working Womble Bungo is convinced he knows it all, even though Great Uncle Bulgaria tells him in no uncertain terms that he knows precious little.

On Bungo's first day of working on the Common Tobermory tells him to watch out for dogs: 'Dogs don't like Wombles, and Wombles don't like dogs.'

But Bungo declares he's not afraid of dogs or anything else. 'More fool you,' mumbles Tobermory. Of course Bungo quickly encounters a large frightening dog and scurries off up a tree as fast as his fat Womble legs will carry him. Orinoco, meanwhile, sits tight on a bench pretending to be asleep, not only failing to be frightened by the dog, but in fact making such bizarre snoring noises that he rather scares off the dog's owner.

Bungo returns astonished and shame-faced – Orinoco's empty tidy bag is filled from Bungo's full one in return for his silence.

It takes another adventure for their friendship to be sealed. Bungo salvages a black umbrella from a pond – he has never seen one before. Orinoco cannot credit such unworldliness but nevertheless shows Bungo how it works. But in mid-demonstration a gust of wind catches him and carries him off the ground, until the umbrella gives out, luckily above the pond. Bungo catches up and drags Orinoco, who is stiff as a board, onto dry land. 'Are you dead?' asks Bungo.

'Yes,' replies Orinoco weakly. 'Oh dear,' says Bungo, beginning to laugh a little. 'It's not at all funny,' says Orinoco, but Bungo laughs till his sides ache.

Bungo is not afraid to take responsibility onto his young shoulders. One day he explores beyond the Common and finds a cement mixer which solves the problem of the hole in the Burrow floors. Then he is volunteered by Great Uncle Bulgaria and Tobermory to venture into central London and find Orinoco. Bungo is quite overwhelmed by London, and his polite ways mean he very nearly can't get off tube trains, let alone onto them. But he sticks to the task well and tracks Orinoco to 'Fortune and Bason's' and with the help of the sudden appearance of Cousin Yellowstone from America they return safe and sound to the Burrow.

When the Burrow on Wimbledon Common threatens to collapse due to the weight of nearby traffic, it is Bungo who is chosen by Great Uncle Bulgaria, with Orinoco as his companion, to head north to Scotland to see if the Wombles can settle there. Bungo takes up the challenge with relish. The only thing he finds difficult is having to keep silent about it to the others, because the operation is so hush hush. All Wombles love to talk, but Bungo especially so.

In Scotland, Bungo and Orinoco are captured by MacWomble the Terrible who takes them for English spies bent on finding out and exploiting a carefully guarded MacWomble secret. Orinoco's strategy in this situation is simple – he says little but manages to deeply impress the MacWomble with his huge appetite. It takes Bungo's fearlessness to get to the bottom of the mystery, the Loch Ness water Womble.

Bungo's intrepid nature, combined with his capacity for having a good laugh, takes him from being the most inexperienced of the working Wombles to the leader of the pack. Orinoco, Wellington and Tomsk fairly follow him around, and don't hesitate to do as he says.

'Alright,' says Bungo to Tomsk. 'Let's take this ladder to Tobermory.' They lift it up. 'One, two, three. March, two three,' says Bungo as he and Tomsk walk indoors.

But Wellington notices Bungo is not actually holding the ladder. 'I count,' explains a grinning Bungo, 'he carries.'

REMEMBER · YOU'RE A WOMBLE

Bungo is always getting himself into scrapes but, partly because he can talk his way out of anything, he never seems to suffer the consequences.

So, even when he gets stuck up a tree the others rush to his rescue and it is Wellington who ends up abandoned 20 feet off the ground and on course for missing dinner.

Bungo grows to be an increasingly respected member of the Womble community. There is only one moment when he falters and becomes a Womble hippy. Great Uncle Bulgaria does nothing, knowing that Bungo will return to his Womble senses eventually – which he does when he sees all the rubbish the hippies leave behind after a pop festival on the Common.

His progress is such that finally Great Uncle Bulgaria grooms him for leadership . . .

Back from the fantastic Wombles' midsummer outing to Battersea fun-fair which had been Bungo's idea, and a year since he had become a working Womble, Bungo looks at the rosy hues of dawn gently filtering across the grass of the Common and Great Uncle Bulgaria comes to stand beside him. 'Bungo,' says Great Uncle Bulgaria putting a paw on his shoulder, 'Not a bad sort of a name. Quite a sensible name really.' And into the burrow they go.

Bungo is truly an adventurer at heart so he is always ready to volunteer for any expedition and never tires of hearing the exploits of older Wombles.

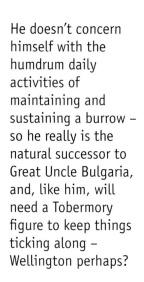

He doesn't concern himself with the humdrum daily activities of maintaining and sustaining a burrow – so he really is the natural successor to Great Uncle Bulgaria, and, like him, will need a Tobermory figure to keep things ticking along – Wellington perhaps?

Bungo's life lessons

Let others see solutions for themselves

As Great Uncle Bulgaria predicts, Bungo comes to his senses and stops being a hippy when he sees rubbish strewn all over the Common after the pop festival.

Learning the virtue of silence is hard, but worth it

Over dinner in the MacWomble Burrow, MacWomble the Terrible grows more pleasant towards the captured Bungo and Orinoco but then fulminates that they certainly can't go home, because they would report back and then the MacWombles would be invaded again. No, they will have to stay.

Bungo has learned there are times to keep quiet, and though the urge to protest is almost too strong he manages to bite his tongue and bide his time.

Find familiarity in the unknown

Bungo is swimming in the loch in the dark. He sees and finally greets the monster. Lovely water for swimming, they agree. 'Are you a Womble too?' asks Bungo. 'Sort of,' replies the monster. 'I'm a water Womble.'

Enjoy childish pleasures

One evening Great Uncle Bulgaria announces he will be giving a story-telling reading. Tomsk, Orinoco and Wellington eagerly abandon what they're doing to attend. Bungo follows, giving a long-suffering sigh in case any of the other Wombles are listening (which they aren't). He meant to go all along, only his dignity wouldn't quite let him do it without a fuss.

He has been a working Womble only a short time so he has a lot of dignity to worry about.

136

Trust your friends

Bungo thinks no one has noticed it is his birthday. So in order to feel really hard-done-by he writes 'as far away as possible,' in the tidying-up area sheet at the burrow's entrance, and nearly adds 'so there' in the margin. When he finds a copy of *The Times*, he decides to stop being dignified for a bit and go back and shake everyone's memories up. Of course they are all highly obtuse. Until they spring his surprise birthday party on him.

Enjoy a game for the game's sake

Bungo doesn't always know best. He loves to win, at pretty much all costs. He likes a good game of Hide the Womble, but Orinoco is no competitor because he always lies down behind a tree and falls asleep. Bungo loves playing it with Tomsk because he's so big he can't hide anywhere well.

Tomsk

**As strong as an ox,
as meek as a lamb.**

Tomsk is sporty, brave, big-hearted, none too
clever, but exceptionally strong. A Womble to have
in times of trouble, Tomsk won't let you down –

so long as he understands what he has to do, of course. And above all, he never gives up.

Big strong Tomsk is an anchor for the other young Wombles – dependable, always there and willing to join in someone's idea. Nevertheless he is very much his own Womble. His passion is sports and he is extremely good at every game he tries, in stark contrast to bookish Wellington, slothful Orinoco and impatient Bungo. All the Wombles know this and respect him for it.

Even Great Uncle Bulgaria learns
how to play golf from him.

But Tomsk also knows there are many things he doesn't know. He understands when to keep silent and just let the others get on with planning whatever it is they are planning. Because he is short on opinions so much of the time, other Wombles have a tendency not to pay him much attention. But no good ever comes from ignoring Tomsk when he starts talking.

Tomsk is in the Burrow contemplating his golf swing. Something catches his eye as he follows through – there is mud on the floor, and it moves. That's odd he says. He calls out to Orinoco to tell him. 'Mud? Hmm, yes, I had a mud pie once,' says Orinoco, wandering off dreamily. Bungo too is not in the mood to listen.

But Tomsk also knows there are many things he doesn't know. He understands when to keep silent and just let the others get on with planning whatever it is they are planning. Because he is short on opinions so much of the time, other Wombles have a tendency not to pay him much attention. But no good ever comes from ignoring Tomsk when he starts talking.

Tomsk is in the Burrow contemplating his golf swing. Something catches his eye as he follows through – there is mud on the floor, and it moves. That's odd he says. He calls out to Orinoco to tell him. 'Mud? Hmm, yes, I had a mud pie once,' says Orinoco, wandering off dreamily. Bungo too is not in the mood to listen.

*Sure enough, there it is. Making steady progress
along the floor. He really had to do something – he
goes out to get a piece of brushwood and a tree
above him sighs and bends over. 'Hey! Don't do that!'
calls out Tomsk. The tree sighs again and leans
towards the roof of the burrow – Tomsk calls out for
help to an unlistening Common and then grabs the
trunk of the tree trying to use all his weight to stop
it plummeting onto the burrow.*

*Tomsk hangs on to the tree for hours and hours as
the cold day settles towards a colder dusk, and then
it begins to rain. And rain and rain. Still Tomsk
hangs on. Bungo and
Orinoco mess about
having a wet paper
fight in the workshop.
Finally when they
are marched to
Great Uncle
Bulgaria's room,
the lights flicker
and cracks start
appearing in the
walls, and
Tobermory realises*

Tomsk goes to the workshop to get a broom, but Tobermory tells him to stop messing about and talking nonsense about moving mud. He bundles him out of the room. Tomsk sighs and goes back to see the mud in motion.

The other Wombles continually under-
estimate Tomsk, but he doesn't let it get
him down, he just surprises them instead.
Even Madame Cholet is amazed, and of
course delighted, by Tomsk's idea of
strapping roller skates to his back paws
and to a wicker panier, the better to
collect overflowing baskets full of
buttercups for buttercup ice-cream.

But Tomsk's finest invention is the creation of a boat to trawl the ponds and lakes for rubbish. This is also when he meets his best Womble friend, a kindred spirit, a Russian Womble called Omsk.

The adventure begins with a swan.

Out on the Common one day industriously picking up rubbish, Tomsk sees a swan in distress, struggling to escape some pernicious rubbish wrapped around its neck. Tomsk doesn't hesitate, but dives in and manages to heave the swan out.

To Tomsk's intense embarrassment the swan then follows him wherever he goes, hero-worshipping him. Meanwhile the other Wombles are finding tidy bags returned to them, full of collected rubbish, accompanied by mysterious notes, signed O.W. Who could it be?

The mystery is solved when Tomsk disappears – he falls into a water channel which carries him miles underwater – and the swan leads the Wombles to Tomsk at which point O.W., Omsk Womble, from Russia reveals himself. He had been guarded because he wasn't sure if the Wombles were friendly. Great Uncle Bulgaria is shocked – all Wombles are friendly!

Omsk is Tomsk's greatest friend and Tomsk is saddened when Omsk returns home to Russia. But then Tomsk voyages around the world with Wellington and meets the Yeti Wombles who he tremendously admires.

Wellington, out of all the other Wombles, is Tomsk's greatest ally. Theirs is a friendship of differences and is no less stable for it. Although they do share a particular trait – in sharp contrast to the self-justifying Orinoco and the self-congratulatory Bungo both are scrupulously truthful.

But although Tomsk is always happy to go along with his fellow Wombles' plans he is not afraid of taking action when he has to, whether it's to rescue the Burrow from falling trees or saving himself and Wellington from exposure in the snowy wastes of Tibet.

Tomsk and Wellington soar over the frozen lands of Siberia and China in their hot air balloon. The air gets colder and colder and suddenly the balloon decides not to fly any more and lands. They sit and shiver. Clever Womble, Wellington, Tomsk thinks, but now he is just sitting there freezing. Perhaps he had better do something. He tries to rouse Wellington, 'Come on, we'll build a snow burrow.' But Wellington doesn't stir, so Tomsk builds it all by himself, then picks Wellington up by the scruff of his neck and shows him the lovely cosy burrow. They get through the night safe and sound and are greeted by the delightful Yeti Wombles the next morning.

Tomsk's life lessons

REMEMBER · YOU'RE A WOMBLE

Listen to voices that rarely speak up

Because he is short on opinions so much of the time, the others have a tendency not to pay much attention to Tomsk. But, as the others discover when the Burrow is nearly smashed by a falling tree, no good comes from ignoring Tomsk when he starts talking.

Value the skills of others

The other Wombles malign Tomsk's interest in golf, but despite the best efforts of Bungo and others, it is Tomsk who manages to get tickets for Great Uncle Bulgaria and Cousin Yellowstone for the Wimbledon tennis championships – by meeting a famous tennis player while out playing golf on the Common.

Take your luck where you find it

The young Wombles are plotting something. Tomsk wants to talk about his new sand wedge but no one will listen. Then something he says gives them an idea. Tomsk has no clue why they are all congratulating him. He goes out to play golf before his luck changes.

Know your limitations

Tomsk hears a great crash and looks up to see the burrow falling in on itself. 'I can't think ahead' he says to himself 'but I can think now!' He quickly props up the ceiling with ladders and then bursts the door open and rushes outside.

Speak your mind

Tomsk isn't a clever sort of Womble but he knows when he is right about things. In Australia Tomsk and Wellington meet formidable Great Great Aunt Murrumbidgee. She greets the young Wombles with gusto and then announces she doesn't know how they can live in Wimbledon, right in the middle of London.

Tomsk dares to contradict her – 'Wimbledon's not in the middle of London. Sorry, but you must have got it mixed up with somewhere else.' Wellington thinks the roof is about to fall in – Aunt Murrumbidgee is like Great Uncle Bulgaria, Tobermory, Miss Adelaide and Madame Cholet all rolled into one. 'Good on you!' says Aunt Murrumbidgee and the ice is truly broken.

The Wombles' Who's Who

Madame Cholet
Mother.
A half-French brilliant cook who took no nonsense from anyone.

Elisabeth Beresford
Each of the Wombles characters is based on someone in the family of Wombles' creator Elisabeth Beresford.

Orinoco
Son, Marcus.
As a BBC reporter Elisabeth and her husband sailed up the Orinoco river.

Bungo
Daughter, Kate.
Bungo knows best.

Great Uncle Bulgaria Coburg Womble
Father-in-law.
The name Coburg pokes fun at Elisabeth's mother's love for European royalty.

Tobermory
Favourite brother,
Aden. *He was terrifically clever.*

Tomsk
A young rather belligerent friend.

Wellington
Nephew.
He went to Wellington college.

Distant relatives

The Wombles of Wimbledon Common journey around the world and meet Wombles everywhere.

The young Womble Alderney helps out Madame Cholet when she visits Wimbledon. She is named after the Channel Island of Alderney, where Elisabeth Beresford lives, and there she is the Womble who keeps beaches clean, and is featured on Alderney's stamps.

Cousin Botany is a rather rough-and-ready Australian Womble who is obsessed with growing underwater plants. Madame Cholet makes them edible and they are known as Botany burgers.

MacWomble the Terrible lives in Loch Ness where his Wombles and Nessie keep the countryside clean. He is a little too fond of the bagpipes for the southern Wombles' taste.

Shansi is a young Womble who chose a Chinese name from Great Uncle Bulgaria's atlas, so she dresses the part too.

As she is a real arts and crafts Womble, Tobermory gives her the task of disguising the Burrow door.

Miss Adelaide is the firm, but kind, head of the Womblegarten where the very young Wombles live before they are old enough to go out on clearing up duty.

The Wombles are serious environmentalists –
everywhere they go they keep the countryside clean
and tidy, their collecting and repairing and re-using
is recycling par excellence. They even raise money
to save windmills from destruction.

Perhaps we should all be a little more like the
Wombles.